JONAS BROTHERS

By Amber P.

Dear valued customer and fellow fan, we would like to express our warmest thanks for your choosing this book. Your support means the world to us as it enables us to come up with more creative contents. Please feel free to leave us a review, we look forward to hearing from you soon!

Introduction

The Jonas Brothers, those teen heartthrobs that sent screaming fans into a crazy tailspin in the mid-2000s with their good looks and sweet songs. Brothers Kevin, Joe and Nick Jonas took on the fame like pros, becoming one of Disney's hottest commodities with their Disney Channel shows and movies, and making chart-topping hit music.

For over a decade, we've been gaga for the Jonas boys, who burst onto the national stage in 2007 and never really left. Sure, the Jonas Brothers broke up and yes, all of them are married. But for some of us, these three brothers will always be a band. Fourteen years have passed, we wanted to ask superfans that: How well do you know the Jonas Brothers?

Do you know the band's name before they settled on **the Jonas Brothers**? If you can answer this question, you're ready for this quiz! Keep reading *Jonas Brothers Trivia Book* to learn facts and play an interesting quiz about this band.

Table of Contents

Introduction...3

A. Trivia questions..5

B. Facts 49

C. Answer key...81

A. Trivia questions

1.   Who is this?

A. Nick
B. Kevin
C. Joe
D. Frankie

2. Who is this?

A. Nick

B. Kevin

C. Joe

D. Frankie

3. Who is this?

A. Nick

B. Kevin

C. Joe

D. Frankie

4. Who is this?

A. Nick

B. Kevin

C. Joe

D. Frankie

5. What is the name of this album?

A. It's About Time
B. Jonas Brothers
C. A Little Bit Longer
D. Lines, Vines and Trying Times

6. What is the name of this album?

A. It's About Time
B. Jonas Brothers
C. A Little Bit Longer
D. Lines, Vines and Trying Times

7. What is the name of this album?

A. It's About Time

B. Jonas Brothers

C. A Little Bit Longer

D. Lines, Vines and Trying Times

8. What is the name of this album?

A. It's About Time

B. Jonas Brothers

C. A Little Bit Longer

D. Lines, Vines and Trying Times

9. What is the name of this album?

A. Wizards of Waverly Place

B. Lizzie McGuire

C. Hannah Montana

D. Camp Rock

10. What is the name of this album?

A. JONAS

B. Lizzie McGuire

C. Hannah Montana

D. Camp Rock

11. What are the Jonas Brothers name in order!!!(oldest to youngest)

    A. Nick, Joe, Kevin
    B. Kevin, Joe, Nick
    C. Frankie, Kevin, Nick
    D. Nick, Kevin, Joe

12. What is Nick's fav song?

    A. When you look me in the eyes
    B. Burnin up
    C. Sos
    D. A little bit longer

13. What is Joe's fav subject in school?

    A. Spelling
    B. Science
    C. Math
    D. Language
    E. Gym

14. What is Kevin's fav ice-cream?

    A. Cotton candy
    B. Chocolate drizzle
    C. Rocky road
    D. Cookies n' cream
    E. He doesn't have one!

15. Which Jonas Brothers got diagnosed with diabetes?

    A. Nick
    B. Joe
    C. Kevin
    D. Frankie
    E. All of them

16. What is Nick's celebrity crush?

    A. Jordan Pruitt
    B. Brenda Song
    C. Miley Cyrus
    D. Camilla Belle

17. What is Joe's celeb crush?

   A. Miley Cyrus
   B. Alecia Ramsay
   C. Demi Lovato
   D. Natilie Portman
   E. Ashley Tisdale

18. Before the boys decided on the name "Jonas Brothers" what were they going to call their band?

   A. Jonas Trio
   B. Sons of Jonas
   C. KJN
   D. None of the above

19. What is Kevin's nickname?

   A. Thunder
   B. Cyclone
   C. K2
   D. PKJ

20. What is Joe's nickname?

    A. Hurricane JJ
    B. JoeJo
    C. Pinkberry
    D. Danger

21. What is Nick's nickname?

    A. Nickman
    B. Mr. President
    C. Wolfman
    D. Rockin NJJ

22. Where were the Jonas Brothers raised?

    A. Montclair, NJ
    B. Winthrop, NJ
    C. Wellington, CA
    D. Wyckoff, NJ

23. What is Mrs. Jonas' first name?

    A. Donna
    B. Denise
    C. Lynn
    D. Mary

24. What is Frankie's (their little brother) nickname?

   A. Little Jonas
   B. Jr Jonas
   C. Frank the tank
   D. Frankman

25. When is Kevin's Birthday?

   A. November 5th
   B. October 15th
   C. October 6th
   D. July 17th

26. When is Joe's Birthday?

   A. June 9th
   B. May 10th
   C. August 15th
   D. December 14th

27. What State was Kevin born in?

   A. Alabama
   B. California
   C. New York
   D. New Jersey

28. What State was Joe born in?

    A. Alaska
    B. Alabama
    C. Arizona
    D. New Jersey

29. What State was Nick born in?

    A. Texas
    B. California
    C. New Jersey
    D. Nevada

30. What are the Jonas Brothers' three favorite cities?

    A. Dallas, Boston, Los Angeles
    B. New York, Dallas, Los Angeles
    C. Boston, New York, Los Angeles

31. What is Joe Jonas's favorite cereal?

    A. Trix
    B. Rice bubbles
    C. Milk cake
    D. Honey nut
    E. Coco pops

32. What is Joe Jonas's middle name?

    A. Brad
    B. Max
    C. Adam
    D. Scott
    E. Nick

33. The youngest Jonas Brothers name is?

    A. Scott
    B. Nick
    C. Kevin
    D. Frankie
    E. Adam

34. What was Nick Jonas diagnosed with?

    A. Diabetes
    B. Singing to much
    C. Downsingdom
    D. No voice

35. What is Kevin's favorite Starbucks drink?

    A. Coffee
    B. Tea
    C. Frozen coffee
    D. Chai latte
    E. Latte

36. For new year's eve 2007 and 2008 where did the Jonas Brothers perform?

    A. Canada
    B. Australia
    C. New York
    D. Gold Coast
    E. China

37. What is the Jonas Brothers' number 1 hit this year?

    A. I wanna be like u
    B. S.O.S
    C. Year 3000
    D. When u look me in the eyes
    E. Hold on

38. Did Nick date Hannah Montana?

    A. Yes
    B. Maybe
    C. Nope
    D. Who is Hannah Montana

39. Which Jonas Brothers was born in Texas?

    A. Kevin
    B. Nick
    C. Joe
    D. Frankie

40. What was the name of the tv show the Jonas Brothers did?

    A. Jonas brothers
    B. JONAS
    C. Brothers forever
    D. Time of our lives

41. What are the Jonas Brothers' parents' names?

   A. John and Sarah
   B. Kevin and Denise
   C. Sam and Mayer
   D. John and Michelle

42. Who is Kevin Jonas married to?

   A. Miley Cyrus
   B. Daniella Delesea
   C. Selena Gomez
   D. Demi Lovato

43. What is Nick and Joe's favorite color?

   A. Green
   B. Black
   C. Blue
   D. Red
   E. Yellow

44. What is Kevin's favorite color?

    A. Blue
    B. Green
    C. Orange
    D. White
    E. Black

45. How many CD's do the Jonas Brothers have?

    A. 2
    B. 1
    C. 5
    D. 4-Including Camp Rock
    E. 100

46. Which Jonas Brother did Broadway musicals?

    A. Kevin
    B. None
    C. Joe
    D. Frankie
    E. Nick

47. Who was on tour with the Jonas Brothers Burning Up tour?

   A. Miley Cyrus
   B. Demi Lovato
   C. Selena Gomez
   D. Rihanna
   E. Jesse Mcartney

48. How long has Kevin Jonas been playing the Guitar?

   A. 20 years
   B. 1 year
   C. 4-5years
   D. 10 years
   E. 6 years

49. Nick Jonas Favorite song from A Little Bit Longer CD?

   A. Tonight
   B. A Little Bit Longer
   C. This is me
   D. Love Bug
   E. Burning up

50. What is Joe Jonas' favorite fruit?

    A. Oranges
    B. Kiwi
    C. Apples
    D. Water Melon
    E. Fruit Roll Up's

51. Jonas Brothers' hometown?

    A. Wycoff, New Jersey
    B. Hollywood, California
    C. New York, New York
    D. Tokyo, Japan
    E. Orlando, Florida

52. When is Nick Jonas's birthday?

    A. December 25th, 1992
    B. September 16th, 1992
    C. November 2nd, 1992
    D. August 20th, 1992

53. The Jonas Brothers weren't always a band, one brother was going it alone and then had the others join on to form a band. Which brother was the solo act to start it all?

A. Nick Jonas

B. Joe Jonas

C. Kevin Jonas

54. The Jonas Brothers care! In 2007, how much money did they contribute to their charity, Change for the Children Foundation?

A. $100,000.00

B. $500,000.00

C. $750,000.00

D. $1,200,000.00

55. The Jonas Brothers love to play games, what is their favorite board game?

A. Trivial Pursuit

B. Monopoly

C. Candy Land

D. Sorry

56. The Jonas Brothers made their acting debut on a fellow musician's Disney Channel show, what was the show?

   A. Wizards of Waverly Place
   B. Lizzie McGuire
   C. Hannah Montana
   D. Sonny With a Chance

57. The Jonas Brothers collaborated with Demi Lovato on which song?

   A. Get back
   B. Live to party
   C. On the line
   D. This is me

58. Which Jonas is said to be the "Bonus Jonas"

   A. Nick
   B. Frankie
   C. Kevin
   D. Joe

59. True or False: Kevin Jonas' real name is Paul

    A. True

    B. False

    C. Others

60. Who is The Jonas Brothers' security guard?

    A. Big Bob

    B. Big Rob

    C. Albert

    D. Quinton

    E. Leroy

61. Nick was gifted a dog for his 16th birthday. What did he name it

    A. Cocco

    B. Manny

    C. Loise

    D. Elvis

    E. Sonny

62. Joe had his own Record Deal

    A. True
    B. False
    C. Others

63. Which Jonas Brother tripped and fell at the 2007 AMA's?

    A. Joe
    B. Frankie
    C. Nick
    D. Kevin

64. What song are the following lyrics from " All this time goes by Still no reason why"?

    A. Shelf
    B. Sorry
    C. A little bit longer
    D. One man show

65. What song did Nick write all by himself?

    A. A little bit longer
    B. Bonus Jonas
    C. Sorry
    D. Got me going crazy

66. What did Nick Jonas write A Little Bit Longer about?

    A. A deceased family member
    B. His disease diabetes
    C. About being on tour
    D. About girlfriends

67. What are the following lyrics from "OMG did you hear I'm dating a Jonas Brother? It's so hot!"?

    A. Lovebug
    B. Pushin' me away
    C. Got me going crazy
    D. Video girl

68. What is the name of the club shown on the cover CD?

    A. Club Jonas
    B. Frankie's club [brother]
    C. Denise's club [mom]
    D. Lovebug club.

69. On the cover "A Little Bit Longer" what are the Jonas Brothers holding?

    A. Kites
    B. Guitars
    C. Microphones
    D. Umbrellas

70. Nick's favorite place in the world is

    A. London
    B. New York City
    C. New Jersey
    D. Chicago
    E. Utah

71. "I miss you more than I did a minute ago/I'd climb a mountain just to hear your echo, you/All I wanted was you" What Jonas Brothers song are these lyrics from?

    A. One Day at a Time
    B. 6 Minutes
    C. You Just Don't Know It
    D. Please Be Mine

72. The Jonas Brothers wrote their first single "Mandy" themselves.

    A. True
    B. False
    C. Others

73. What is the name of Nick's rap?

    A. Nick J is Off the Chain
    B. Nick J loves his Chain
    C. Nick J is On the Chain
    D. Nick J hates Chains

74. What song did the Jonas Brothers remake from "The Little Mermaid"?

    A. Kiss the Girl
    B. Part of Your World
    C. Under the Sea
    D. Poor Unfortunate Souls

75. What song are these lyrics from... "She's the kinda girl that you see in the movies/Seen her in my dreams and now she's standing next to me/Down by the shore, first weekend of the summer/Got to take a chance and just ask for her number"

    A. 6 Minutes
    B. You Just don't Know it
    C. Mandy
    D. 7:05

76. What song are these lyrics from?... "Told you I made dinner plans, with you and me and no one else. That don't include your crazy friends"

    A. S.O.S.
    B. Hollywood
    C. Games
    D. I Wanna Be Like You

77. What song is this from?... "Not much has changed, but they lived underwater, and your great, great, great grand-daughter, is doin' fine!"

    A. Games
    B. Year 2000
    C. Year 3000
    D. Year 1000

78. Are these the correct lyrics to the song, "Hollywood"?... "As Time was tickin' we were on time, and it all was goin' as planned, found the schedule on my dresser, and now were making headlines, street signs saying you're on the right track, so go faster now!..."

    A. True
    B. False
    C. Others

79. What song is this from?... "Everyone knows it's meant to be, falling in love with you and me, 'till the end of time 'till I'm on your mind it'll happen, I've been making lots of plans, like a picket fence and a rose garden, I'll just keep on dreamin'..."

   A. Somewhere Over The Rainbow
   B. Just Friends
   C. Australia
   D. Inseparable

80. What song is this?...: "The one that never said a word, but she always sang, SClub7 and all those boy bands. Now it's been a few years it looks like things have changed, now she's mine and I want to say!...."

   A. Jordyn
   B. Jennifer
   C. Mandy
   D. Moranda

81. What song are these lyrics from?...: "Cause an empty room, can be so loud there's too many tears, to drown them out..."

A. Frankie
B. Kids Of The Future
C. That's Just The Way We Roll
D. Hold On

82. What song are these lyrics from?... "Take my hand tonight, we can run so far, we can change the world, to anything we want, we could run forever, if you wanted to, I would not get tired, because I'd be with you, I'd keep singing this song until the very end..."

A. Underdog
B. Goodnight & Goodbye
C. Inseparable
D. One Day At A Time

83. What song is this from?... "You never listen to me, I know I'm better off alone. Everybody knows it's true, yeah we all see through you, and it won't be hard to do..."

    A. S.O.S
    B. Australia
    C. You Can't Stop The Beat
    D. What I Go To School For

84. What song are these lyrics from? "Life isn't suffocating, Air isn't overrated"

    A. You Just Don't Know It
    B. Games
    C. Take A Breath
    D. Australia

85. The following lyrics are from which Jonas Brothers song? "We will live in the light of the sun again, Dancing in the river of life"

    A. Please Be Mine
    B. Still In Love With You
    C. One Day At A Time
    D. Eternity

86. "Maybe she'll be in a movie, Maybe she'll be in a song, Better pay her some attention- Before she's gone" are lyrics from the song?

    A. Underdog
    B. I Am What I Am
    C. 6 Minutes
    D. Hollywood

87. The following lyrics are from what song? "You don't know what you got 'til it's gone, you don't know what it's like to feel so low."

    A. Goodnight and Goodbye
    B. Time For Me To Fly
    C. Inseparable
    D. A Little Bit Longer

88. What song are these lyrics from? "When I hold you in my arms, I know that it's forever"

    A. When You Look Me In The Eyes
    B. Please Be Mine
    C. Hold On
    D. Inseparable

89. Who wrote the song, "SOS"?

    A. Nick
    B. Kevin
    C. Joe
    D. They wrote it together

90. What song is this line from? "But tonight, I'm gonna fly."

    A. Time for Me to Fly
    B. Take a Breath
    C. S.O.S.
    D. Hello Beautiful

91. What is the missing lyric? "Can you feel it in the way I look at you? Girl, can you hear it? I'm crying out ..."

    A. to you
    B. inside
    C. for you
    D. loud

92. What are the missing lyrics, "Fallen soldiers all around us, but we're still ... ..."?

A. hanging on
B. walking strong
C. moving on
D. standing strong

93. What is the missing lyric, "Oh I was so ... Now I know you love me. This right here is how I feel"?

A. blind
B. depressed
C. lonely
D. unsure

94. What are the missing lyrics, "I recall all our fights. Most of all, all the times you would lie ... ... Now you're gone."?

A. to my face
B. in my arms
C. next to me
D. by my side

95. What are the missing lyrics, "The two of us tonight, we can make it last forever. We're in the neon lights. It's just you and me together. Hollywood is .. ... The stars are shining for you and me tonight in this city"?

    A. on fire
    B. right here
    C. the time
    D. the town

96. What are the missing lyric(s), "Love, I've finally found a new one and it came to me in such a vision. Now I know I need you so. You make me burn like ..."?

    A. fire
    B. sun rays
    C. flames
    D. crazy

97. What is the missing lyric, "This party's ... and now I'm running out of time. I've only got six minutes if I'm gonna make her mine."?

    A. lame
    B. late
    C. ending
    D. closing

98. What are the missing lyrics, "Hey baby, what's the matter with you? Hey darlin', know your love is.. ... I'm going crazy"?

A. for fools
B. n't new
C. a tool
D. n't true

99. What is the missing lyric(s), "Dreamers, you see everything in color while the world is getting ... Love is on its way"?

A. louder
B. colder
C. darker
D. brighter

100. What are the missing lyrics, "Like a meteor I'm falling. From the first time ... ... It was heaven on Earth."?

A. we both met
B. I saw her
C. we locked eyes
D. our hands touched

101. "Waiting on a cure, but none of them are sure," What song are these lyrics from?

    A. Turn Right
    B. A Little Bit Longer
    C. BB Good
    D. Black Keys

102. "I gave my all for you, now my heart's in two." Can you name this song?

    A. SOS
    B. Burnin' Up
    C. Hold On
    D. Heart and Soul

103. "If you recall, our anniversary falls eleven nights into June." What song is this from?

    A. First Time
    B. Wedding Bells
    C. When You Look Me In the Eyes
    D. Games

104. "Wanna dance until my feet can't feel the ground."
What song is this from?

A. Hold On
B. Keep It Real
C. Play My Music
D. BB Good

105. "It's not that hard to be a friend." Can you name the song?

A. Black Keys
B. A Little Bit Longer
C. SOS
D. Hold On

106. "If false turns out to be true, you know that I will find you, because our love is destiny." What song is this from?

A. First Time
B. Infatuation
C. When You Look Me In The Eyes
D. Mandy

107. "Even though she is the blonde, I'm the one who feels so dumb." Can you name the song?

A. Paranoid
B. One Day At a Time
C. Mandy
D. World War 3

108. "I'll pick you up at seven, we can drive around and see a movie." Can you name the song?

A. Australia
B. Mandy
C. BB Good
D. Burnin' Up

109. "I've been looking for that someone, I'll never make it on my own." Which song is this from?

A. Invisible
B. When You Look Me In the Eyes
C. Gotta Find You
D. Can't Have You

110. "Somehow I'm to blame for this never-ending racetrack you call life." In which song would you find these lyrics?

A. Black Keys
B. Poison Ivy
C. World War 3
D. Turn Right

B. Facts

1. While they have a lot in common—such as being homeschooled by their mom—all three Jonas brothers were born in different US states. Kevin (b. 1987) was born in New Jersey, Joe (b. 1989) in Arizona, and Nick (b. 1992) in Texas.

2. Not unlike the Three Musketeers, there exists a fourth Jonas brother. Frankie Jonas was born in 2000 and is sometimes referred to as the "Bonus Jonas" or "Biff." He is also an actor—his first role in a film was voicing the character Sosuke in the English dub of the Studio Ghibli film Ponyo.

3. In 2008, the Jonas Brothers became the youngest band to make the cover of Rolling Stone magazine. Take that, The Beatles!

4. Being Kevin Jonas ain't all it's cracked up to be. For one, his name isn't even Kevin. He was named after his father, Paul Jonas Sr. Everything we know is a lie!

5. The Jonas Brothers had an old band name, which they hated. Originally called "J3," the trio had a last-minute change of heart right before their first concert tour. Joe asked his brothers, "Do you want our name to be J3 for the rest of our lives?" They did not. Thus, at the next show, Joe was the first to declare to the audience, "Hey, we're the Jonas Brothers." That was easy.

6. When the band broke up in 2013, Nick Jonas was the first to bring up the topic. Joe was the most vocally resistant.

7. Joe Jonas recorded a solo album that, in his words, never "saw the light of day." According to Joe, the unheard record took heavy inspiration from Hall & Oates, as well as Freddy Mercury. Apparently, punk-rock has been his favorite genre since childhood, so it's understandable that he'd try to branch out from his pop roots.

8. With four studio albums under the belt, countless hours of touring, a Grammy nomination, and two Disney Channel original movies, the Jonas Brothers

decided to go on a hiatus in 2011. During this time, Nick Jonas continued working on his first solo career with a band he titled Nick Jonas & the Administration. Meanwhile, Joe Jonas focused on his own solo career with a more R&B inspired album entitled Fastlife. Eldest brother Kevin took a break from the world of touring to spend time with his new wife while also studying music production.

9. The "purity" rings were a huge part of the Jonas Brothers' image. "Proudly" displaying their abstinence, the accessories were a natural culmination of the Disney brand, who wanted the boys to be pristine—the ultimate family-friendly icons. It goes without saying, all three brothers have done away with the bling.

10. In a 2016 Reddit AMA, Joe Jonas admitted he broke the "vow" represented by his brothers' rings. When he was 20, he slept with someone for the first time—his then-girlfriend, Ashley Greene of the Twilight series. Joe did put "safety first, kids" (his words) by basically demolishing his drummer's room in search of contraception.

11. In 2016, Joe confessed to smoking illegal substances with Disney Channel colleagues Miley Cyrus and Demi Lovato.

12. In general, Joe has expressed anxiety about toxic drugs. This is partly a leftover of his tightly-controlled Disney days. When he tried drinking for the first time at the age of 17, he "thought the world was going to collapse" until he remembered they were in a country where it was legal. For his 21st birthday, Joe really got a little too loose and fell down a flight of stairs. Knocked unconscious, his entourage and team were deathly

scared that someone would take a picture and cause a scandal. Oh, and that he was unconscious was concerning too, I hope.

13. Joe Jonas and his Camp Rock co-star Demi Lovato really dated for a month. However, Jonas was quite unhappy for most of it, partly due to Lovato's substance issues. Joe admits he kept things together for the brand, but he felt trapped nevertheless. Unfortunately, fans were really invested in the stars' relationship, which also put pressure on them to make it work out.

14. Nick Jonas recalls an awkward date with Disney cohort member Selena Gomez. The pair went to Central Park, but—for reasons that remain unclear to us—Nick preferred to walk about 20-25 feet apart from her the whole time. He admits it "ruined" her first time in the iconic park.

15. We all know Taylor Swift's version of her breakup with Joe Jonas. According to Swift, Joe dumped her via a 30-second phone call and promptly started seeing actress Camilla Belle. Joe's version (revealed in the most 2008 way: MySpace)? The relationship (and conversation) was cut-off because "phone calls can only last as long as the person on the other end of the line is willing to talk."

16. While rumors had been percolating for years, a Jonas Brothers reunion finally happened in February of 2019, seven years after the band had called it quits. The reunion was announced via social media and on March 1st Jonas Brothers fans were listening to the band's first single "Sucker."

17. In an interview, Joe Jonas admitted that he "took advantage of the opportunities" to date fans during the height of his fame. At the age of 16, he invited a fan to a movie, where the two "just made out the entire time."

18. The Jonas Brothers met 007? Shocking but true. Their Disney Channel sitcom Jonas was originally to be titled "J.O.N.A.S." for "Junior Operatives Networking As Spies." By the time the show went into production, after the 2007-08 Writers' Strike, the premise was reworked to be more "at home" with the music-industry focused antics of Disney sitcoms like Hannah Montana and Sonny With a Chance, which meant trading in the gadgets for guitars.

19. Joe has complained that the Jonas sitcom had him shave every day to convincingly play a 16-year-old... even though he was 20.

20. When FIFA corruption met Paul McCartney and money laundering, there entered Kevin Jonas, ready to testify for the prosecution. In 2017, the eldest Jonas brother was ordered to testify in court regarding a 2010 bribery scandal. Juan Angel Napout was accused of money laundering, racketeering, and wire fraud. In his defense, Napout's lawyers denied that a certain Paul McCartney concert ever took place. Kevin was called in to help establish a timeframe and argued, yes, the concert in question did happen.

21. In 2014, Kevin Jonas and his wife Danielle Delisa announced that they were pregnant with their first child. Fans literally thought this was too good to be true. A "fake pregnancy" conspiracy circulated, and users obsessively picked apart posts to suggest this was a hoax. When their daughter Alana was born anyways, this still did not give up. One fan even went back to an earlier social media post to argue that a 15-week ultrasound depicted a fully-grown fetus, ergo... the baby was fake?

22. Considering their roots in Christian rock (and those purity rings), it's little surprise that the Jonas Brothers are Christian. However, the family left the Church in their early teens due to a stolen money scandal. Now they are, in Joe's words, "not religious in any way".

23. In 2015, Joe Jonas began to date model Gigi Hadid. Did we mention Hadid was one of the best friends of his ex, Taylor Swift? Who says high school has to end?

24. Columbia Records, the band's first label, initially had little faith in the brothers' debut album—and the feeling was mutual. In fact, the brothers felt really unsupported at Columbia and hoped to leave soon for a new label. Columbia gave their first album a limited release—only 50,000 copies. That little first album would go on to sell 1.75 million copies.

25. Before their sitcom, the Jonas Brothers got their acting big break thanks to Miley Cyrus. Their acting debut was in a Hannah Montana episode! The episode was seen by over ten million people and became the most-watched basic cable broadcast in television history.

26. While their 3D biopic Jonas Brothers: The 3D Concert Experience (2009) is the sixth high-grossing concert film of all time, the follow-up album failed to meet the same success. Lines, Vines and Trying Times "only" sold one million copies in the US.

27. After 2009, the Jonas Brothers spent some time apart to explore solo projects. In Nick's case, that included Broadway (but only after his solo album became a commercial failure). He played Marius Pontmercy in the West End showing of Les Misérables. Originally, he was only to be performing for three weeks, but the

continued hiatus of the Jonas Brothers enabled him to extend his run another month.

28. At the age of 13, Nick Jonas was diagnosed with Type I diabetes. In 2009, he testified before the US Senate to lobby for more funding towards diabetes research.

29. On 18 July 2018, Nick Jonas became engaged to Quantico actress Priyanka Chopra. The two had a traditional Punjabi Roka engagement ceremony in August.

30. Nick isn't the only Jonas Brother to couple up with a small-screen star. In October 2017, Joe Jonas announced his engagement to Game of Thrones actress Sophie Turner.

31. Kevin is the oldest and most lowkey of his brothers, at least when it comes to being in the spotlight. After the split, Kevin didn't turn towards music and film like his brothers, but he instead focused on business ventures. His portfolio includes founding a construction company (of all things) called JonasWerner, being the co-CEO of the communications company The Blu Market, creating

the Yood food app, and entering a partnership with We Heart It in 2016.

32. Kevin Jonas and his wife starred in their own E! reality series, Married to Jonas. Unfortunately, the show only lasted two seasons. At least that's more time to look after all those businesses?

33. In a 2008 interview, Joe Jonas revealed his favorite book was A Wrinkle in Time by Madeleine L'Engle. Hope he liked the movie that came out only ten years later.

34. In 2002, Nick Jonas made his musical debut as Chip in the stage version of Beauty and the Beast. At nine years old, then "Nicholas Jonas" took over the role from another actor for the last few months of the musical's run.

35. Joe Jonas auditioned for the role of Justin Russo in Wizards of Waverly Place. Considering the star, Selena Gomez, dated his brother Nick, Joe's subpar acting skills might have saved him a few seasons of awkwardness.

36. The Jonas Brothers' dad was himself a songwriter and musician. Of course, he did not reach the same heights of fame as his sons, but he did become an ordained minister with the Assemblies of God.

37. In 2012, Nick got the honor of replacing Daniel Radcliffe in an iconic franchise. Not Harry Potter, but rather the Broadway show How to Succeed in Business Without Really Trying.

38. Joe Jonas actually loves the 2009 South Park episode that makes fun of them, the purity rings, and the whole Disney company. While their manager at the time forbade reporters from asking them about it, the

brothers watched and enjoyed it. Wait, doesn't Mickey Mouse brutally beat Joe in that episode? Yes, and while Nick isn't a fan, Joe loves that part especially.

39. Nick and Joe were living together when Nick got a part in the Jumanji remake. So while his younger brother was off making movies, Joe made liberal use of his wardrobe. Is clothes budgeting still a problem at this stage?

40. Joe Jonas admits to modeling his peak-Jonas Bros hair after the lead singer from the band Tokio Hotel's anime style. It took him 30 minutes a day to get just right.

41. Nick Jonas is most embarrassed about their song "Pizza Girl," which they wrote for their show. For one, the premise is kind of ridiculous; it was the network who ordered the brothers to write a song where "you fall in love with the pizza girl and then you eat pizza every day." Not exactly dramatic stuff. Nick also laments how they couldn't even get it to rhyme.

42. The Jonas Brothers' breakup shocked fans everywhere, but according to Joe, it was a long time coming. They were no longer "jelling" in the studio. Likewise, it became clear that the brothers themselves wanted to go in different creative directions. Yelling at each other, it was one vague "band-breaking" argument that finally broke the well-coiffed camel's back.

43. Nick got his driver's license on the same day that the band shot the album cover for "Lines, Vines and Trying Times," the Jonas Brothers' fourth album. The album was released in June 2009 and was the last one that band put out before their 2013 breakup. "Lines, Vines and Trying Times" featured "Paranoid," their duet with Miley Cyrus called "Before the Storm," and "Fly with Me" (which was played during the end credits of "Night at the Museum 2: Battle of the Smithsonian").

44. Joe said that he was embarrassed by his flat-ironed hair and dance moves that were on display in "Camp Rock". He added: "When I see old merchandise from 'Camp Rock' days or somebody is like, 'Oh my god, "Camp Rock" is my jam,' I really have a hard time believing them".

45. Kevin met now-wife Danielle Jonas (née Deleasa) in 2007, when both of their families were on vacation in the Bahamas. The couple got engaged two years later and tied the knot at Oheka Castle in New York in December 2009. They now have two daughters

together: Alena Rose (born in February 2014) and Valentina Angelina (born in October 2016).

46. Nick has a scar on his left middle finger from a pocket knife accident that happened when he was 9 years old. "That was a mistake. I should not have had the pocket knife that day," he said in a segment for MTV called "100 Things You Didn't Know."

47. Joe's dream duet would be with music icon Barbra Streisand.

48. Kevin is the subject of a meme called "Lonely Kevin". Joe explained the origin of the meme, which shows Kevin standing on a sidewalk with a phone in one hand and a somewhat confused expression, during his 2016 Reddit AMA. Joe went on to say that Kevin was probably not fond of the meme at first, but he has since come to "appreciate" it. The Jonas Brothers also poked fun at the Internet joke while performing an updated version of "Year 3000" on CBS' "Late Late Show With James Corden" in March 2019.

49. Nick and Joe have matching arrow tattoos on their arms. They got the ink on their triceps right before attending the 2016 MTV Video Music Awards and documented it on social media. Nick also has a tattoo

that reads "God is greater than the highs and lows" and another one that says "Mercy".

50. Kevin and Danielle chose Nick to be the godfather of their second child, Valentina. Both Nick and Joe are proud uncles. When the siblings appeared on "The Late Late Show," Kevin said that Valentina is "territorial" over Nick and was especially protective when she met Priyanka Chopra, Nick's now-wife.

51. Nick and Joe have named Daniel Craig as their celebrity crush. Nick revealed his crush on the "Bond" actor

during a 2014 interview with Cosmopolitan, while Joe said it during his AMA.

52. Joe said that he first tried marijuana with fellow former Disney stars Demi Lovato and Miley Cyrus. "I must have been 17 or 18," he said in a 2013 tell-all for New York Magazine called "Joe Jonas: My Life as a Jonas Brother." "They kept saying, 'Try it! Try it!,' so I gave it a shot, and it was all right. I don't even smoke weed that often anymore."

53. Nick was in a Chuck E. Cheese commercial when he was a child. You can see the commercial, which shows a young Nick in a backward baseball cap and a yellow and gray shirt, here. Kevin also appeared in ads for Office Depot, Burger King, and other brands.

54. They didn't hang out with only each other for almost 6 years. Chasing Happiness starts off with the three bros reuniting and remarking upon how long it's been since the three of them spent quality time alone together. At different points in the film, they say that it had been six or seven years.

55. Joe wanted to be a comedian as a kid. Nick, Joe, and Kevin each reminisce about their childhoods and past aspirations. It turns out that Joe wanted to be on All That or perform stand-up comedy, which makes a lot of sense.

56. They repaired their damaged relationship in Australia. The truly raw and honest conversations that the documentary shows went down in Sydney in 2018, when the brothers were traveling and reconnecting, including the truth-telling drinking game they spoke about in the press after the reunion was announced.

57. Kevin was bullied in school. Kevin says that because of his "uncool" hobbies (magic, gymnastics) and the inexpensive clothes he wore, he "became a target" of his classmates. "They would call me 'gay,' they would call me 'f*g,' they would call me 'pisshead,'" he said. He got involved in commercial acting partly because he didn't feel like he "connected" at school.

58. Nick got a record deal through a christmas song. For the Christian family, a Christmas song was the perfect entrance into the professional music world. "Joy to the World (A Christmas Prayer)", co-written by Nick and his father, Kevin Jonas Sr., made its way to manager David Massey when Nick was just 10 years old. Massey appears in the doc and says he saw something special in Nick.

59. The family kept their work a secret from their church. You may know that their father was a pastor, but you probably didn't realize that the family had worried about the community response to the band singing secular music and working with a secular label.

60. The Jonas Brothers were originally supposed to be a punk rock band. They found a backing band and rehearsed intensively to fit the rock image the label wanted. Nick mentions that there's a misconception that the band was "manufactured" by Disney, but they weren't even involved with the company at this point.

61. Nick's moodiness led, in part, to his diabetes diagnosis. Their father tells the camera that the backing band told him that Nick's attitude was becoming an issue. Also, when the band was driving from show to show, Nick would constantly have to stop for giant sodas and to use the bathroom. These were symptoms of his diabetes, which, for a time, they kept a secret from their label.

62. Their father had to leave his job. Once the band became more popular, Kevin Sr. was encouraged to resign from his post. That led the family into a period of financial hardship, made worse when Columbia dropped the Jonas brothers from the label. Their parents had put their savings into the band, so the whole clan moved into a two-bedroom house in Little Falls, New Jersey.

63. They wrote their (first) comeback album in the little falls house. From their lowest point in life, the band wrote some of the biggest songs in their career, which came "out of the pain and the hurt and the abandonment," Joe says. That became the Jonas Brothers album, which was released after they were signed to Disney's Hollywood Records.

64. 'Camp Rock' wasn't supposed to star the whole band. Joe had been cast as the lead of Camp Rock. Their father called the president of the Disney Channel to suggest that they include Kevin and Nick as well. And the rest is DCOM history.

65. The brothers "hated each other" for a time. After Nick and Joe's solo efforts, the band tried to regroup for their next album, but their new singles weren't hitting with fans. "We lost sight of the fact that we were just a band having a good time," Kevin says. "People liked seeing us happy and we were not happy." Nick says that, as they prepared for a new tour, things were really tough. "We hated each other, basically."

C. Answer key

1. A	21. B	41. B	61. D	81. D	101. B
2. C	22. D	42. B	62. B	82. C	102. A
3. B	23. B	43. C	63. A	83. B	103. B
4. D	24. C	44. B	64. C	84. C	104. C
5. A	25. A	45. C	65. A	85. D	105. D
6. D	26. C	46. E	66. B	86. A	106. B
7. C	27. D	47. B	67. D	87. D	107. C
8. B	28. C	48. C	68. B	88. A	108. C
9. D	29. A	49. D	69. D	89. A	109. B
10. A	30. C	50. C	70. D	90. D	110. D
11. B	31. A	51. A	71. A	91. B	
12. D	32. C	52. C	72. A	92. D	
13. C	33. D	53. A	73. A	93. C	
14. C	34. A	54. D	74. D	94. B	
15. A	35. D	55. B	75. B	95. C	
16. D	36. C	56. C	76. A	96. D	
17. D	37. C	57. C	77. C	97. A	
18. B	38. C	58. B	78. B	98. D	
19. C	39. B	59. A	79. B	99. C	
20. D	40. B	60. B	80. C	100. B